Foundation Table Book

By J. Noel

Philograph Publications Limited   Andover   Hants

Contents

How to spell the numbers

0	nought (also called zero)	17	seventeen
1	one	18	eighteen
2	two	19	nineteen
3	three	20	twenty
4	four	21	twenty-one
5	five	22	twenty-two
6	six	30	thirty
7	seven	40	forty
8	eight	50	fifty
9	nine	60	sixty
10	ten	70	seventy
11	eleven	80	eighty
12	twelve	90	ninety
13	thirteen	100	hundred
14	fourteen	1 000	thousand
15	fifteen	10 000	ten thousand
16	sixteen	1 000 000	million

$1 \times$	$\times 1$
$1 \times 0 = 0$	$0 \times 1 = 0$
$1 \times 1 = 1$	$1 \times 1 = 1$
$1 \times 2 = 2$	$2 \times 1 = 2$
$1 \times 3 = 3$	$3 \times 1 = 3$
$1 \times 4 = 4$	$4 \times 1 = 4$
$1 \times 5 = 5$	$5 \times 1 = 5$
$1 \times 6 = 6$	$6 \times 1 = 6$
$1 \times 7 = 7$	$7 \times 1 = 7$
$1 \times 8 = 8$	$8 \times 1 = 8$
$1 \times 9 = 9$	$9 \times 1 = 9$
$1 \times 10 = 10$	$10 \times 1 = 10$

$2 \times$	$\times 2$
$2 \times 0 = 0$	$0 \times 2 = 0$
$2 \times 1 = 2$	$1 \times 2 = 2$
$2 \times 2 = 4$	$2 \times 2 = 4$
$2 \times 3 = 6$	$3 \times 2 = 6$
$2 \times 4 = 8$	$4 \times 2 = 8$
$2 \times 5 = 10$	$5 \times 2 = 10$
$2 \times 6 = 12$	$6 \times 2 = 12$
$2 \times 7 = 14$	$7 \times 2 = 14$
$2 \times 8 = 16$	$8 \times 2 = 16$
$2 \times 9 = 18$	$9 \times 2 = 18$
$2 \times 10 = 20$	$10 \times 2 = 20$

3 ×	× 3
3 × 0 = 0	0 × 3 = 0
3 × 1 = 3	1 × 3 = 3
3 × 2 = 6	2 × 3 = 6
3 × 3 = 9	3 × 3 = 9
3 × 4 = 12	4 × 3 = 12
3 × 5 = 15	5 × 3 = 15
3 × 6 = 18	6 × 3 = 18
3 × 7 = 21	7 × 3 = 21
3 × 8 = 24	8 × 3 = 24
3 × 9 = 27	9 × 3 = 27
3 × 10 = 30	10 × 3 = 30

4 ×	× 4
4 × 0 = 0	0 × 4 = 0
4 × 1 = 4	1 × 4 = 4
4 × 2 = 8	2 × 4 = 8
4 × 3 = 12	3 × 4 = 12
4 × 4 = 16	4 × 4 = 16
4 × 5 = 20	5 × 4 = 20
4 × 6 = 24	6 × 4 = 24
4 × 7 = 28	7 × 4 = 28
4 × 8 = 32	8 × 4 = 32
4 × 9 = 36	9 × 4 = 36
4 × 10 = 40	10 × 4 = 40

5 ×	× 5
5 × 0 = 0	0 × 5 = 0
5 × 1 = 5	1 × 5 = 5
5 × 2 = 10	2 × 5 = 10
5 × 3 = 15	3 × 5 = 15
5 × 4 = 20	4 × 5 = 20
5 × 5 = 25	5 × 5 = 25
5 × 6 = 30	6 × 5 = 30
5 × 7 = 35	7 × 5 = 35
5 × 8 = 40	8 × 5 = 40
5 × 9 = 45	9 × 5 = 45
5 × 10 = 50	10 × 5 = 50

$6 \times$	$\times 6$
$6 \times 0 = 0$	$0 \times 6 = 0$
$6 \times 1 = 6$	$1 \times 6 = 6$
$6 \times 2 = 12$	$2 \times 6 = 12$
$6 \times 3 = 18$	$3 \times 6 = 18$
$6 \times 4 = 24$	$4 \times 6 = 24$
$6 \times 5 = 30$	$5 \times 6 = 30$
$6 \times 6 = 36$	$6 \times 6 = 36$
$6 \times 7 = 42$	$7 \times 6 = 42$
$6 \times 8 = 48$	$8 \times 6 = 48$
$6 \times 9 = 54$	$9 \times 6 = 54$
$6 \times 10 = 60$	$10 \times 6 = 60$

$7 \times$	$\times 7$
$7 \times 0 = 0$	$0 \times 7 = 0$
$7 \times 1 = 7$	$1 \times 7 = 7$
$7 \times 2 = 14$	$2 \times 7 = 14$
$7 \times 3 = 21$	$3 \times 7 = 21$
$7 \times 4 = 28$	$4 \times 7 = 28$
$7 \times 5 = 35$	$5 \times 7 = 35$
$7 \times 6 = 42$	$6 \times 7 = 42$
$7 \times 7 = 49$	$7 \times 7 = 49$
$7 \times 8 = 56$	$8 \times 7 = 56$
$7 \times 9 = 63$	$9 \times 7 = 63$
$7 \times 10 = 70$	$10 \times 7 = 70$

8 ×	× 8
8 × 0 = 0	0 × 8 = 0
8 × 1 = 8	1 × 8 = 8
8 × 2 = 16	2 × 8 = 16
8 × 3 = 24	3 × 8 = 24
8 × 4 = 32	4 × 8 = 32
8 × 5 = 40	5 × 8 = 40
8 × 6 = 48	6 × 8 = 48
8 × 7 = 56	7 × 8 = 56
8 × 8 = 64	8 × 8 = 64
8 × 9 = 72	9 × 8 = 72
8 × 10 = 80	10 × 8 = 80

9 ×	× 9
9 × 0 = 0	0 × 9 = 0
9 × 1 = 9	1 × 9 = 9
9 × 2 = 18	2 × 9 = 18
9 × 3 = 27	3 × 9 = 27
9 × 4 = 36	4 × 9 = 36
9 × 5 = 45	5 × 9 = 45
9 × 6 = 54	6 × 9 = 54
9 × 7 = 63	7 × 9 = 63
9 × 8 = 72	8 × 9 = 72
9 × 9 = 81	9 × 9 = 81
9 × 10 = 90	10 × 9 = 90

10 ×	× 10
10 × 0 = 0	0 × 10 = 0
10 × 1 = 10	1 × 10 = 10
10 × 2 = 20	2 × 10 = 20
10 × 3 = 30	3 × 10 = 30
10 × 4 = 40	4 × 10 = 40
10 × 5 = 50	5 × 10 = 50
10 × 6 = 60	6 × 10 = 60
10 × 7 = 70	7 × 10 = 70
10 × 8 = 80	8 × 10 = 80
10 × 9 = 90	9 × 10 = 90
10 × 10 = 100	10 × 10 = 100

A table of addition facts

10	10	11	12	13	14	15	16	17	18	19	20
9	9	10	11	12	13	14	15	16	17	18	19
8	8	9	10	11	12	13	14	15	16	17	18
7	7	8	9	10	11	12	13	14	15	16	17
6	6	7	8	9	10	11	12	13	14	15	16
5	5	6	7	8	9	10	11	12	13	14	15
4	4	5	6	7	8	9	10	11	12	13	14
3	3	4	5	6	7	8	9	10	11	12	13
2	2	3	4	5	6	7	8	9	10	11	12
1	1	2	3	4	5	6	7	8	9	10	11
0	0	1	2	3	4	5	6	7	8	9	10
+	0	1	2	3	4	5	6	7	8	9	10

Counting on in multiples

2	4	6	8	10	12	14	16	18	20
3	6	9	12	15	18	21	24	27	30
4	8	12	16	20	24	28	32	36	40
5	10	15	20	25	30	35	40	45	50
6	12	18	24	30	36	42	48	54	60
7	14	21	28	35	42	49	56	63	70
8	16	24	32	40	48	56	64	72	80
9	18	27	36	45	54	63	72	81	90
10	20	30	40	50	60	70	80	90	100

Box Table   1 × 1 to 10 × 10

×	1	2	3	4	5	6	7	8	9	10
10	10	20	30	40	50	60	70	80	90	100
9	9	18	27	36	45	54	63	72	81	90
8	8	16	24	32	40	48	56	64	72	80
7	7	14	21	28	35	42	49	56	63	70
6	6	12	18	24	30	36	42	48	54	60
5	5	10	15	20	25	30	35	40	45	50
4	4	8	12	16	20	24	28	32	36	40
3	3	6	9	12	15	18	21	24	27	30
2	2	4	6	8	10	12	14	16	18	20
1	1	2	3	4	5	6	7	8	9	10

Square numbers

$1^2 = 1 \times 1 = 1$

$2^2 = 2 \times 2 = 4$

$3^2 = 3 \times 3 = 9$

$4^2 = 4 \times 4 = 16$

$5^2 = 5 \times 5 = 25$

$6^2 = 6 \times 6 = 36$

$7^2 = 7 \times 7 = 49$

$8^2 = 8 \times 8 = 64$

$9^2 = 9 \times 9 = 81$

$10^2 = 10 \times 10 = 100$

Putting figures in the right places

h 100	t 10	u 1	h = hundred t = ten u = unit or one
		1	1 = 1 one unit
	1	0	10 + 0 = 10 one ten + no units
1	0	0	100 + 0 + 0 = 100 one hundred + no tens + no units
	4	1	40 + 1 = 41 four tens + one unit
1	1	1	100 + 10 + 1 = 111 one hundred + one ten + one unit
	2	7	20 + 7 = 27 two tens + seven units
6	5	0	600 + 50 + 0 = 650 six hundreds + five tens + no units

Numeration and place value

units	1
tens	12
hundreds	123
thousands	1 234
tens of thousands	12 345
hundreds of thousands	123 456
millions	1 234 567
tens of millions	12 345 678
hundreds of millions	123 456 789

Signs and Symbols

Sign		Example
=	is equal to	$2 + 3 = 3 + 2$
+	plus or add	$4 + 6 = 10$
−	minus or subtract	$10 - 4 = 6$
×	multiply	$5 \times 2 = 10$
÷	divide	$10 \div 2 = 5$
>	larger than	$70 > 68$
<	smaller than	$68 < 70$
°	degree	$65°$
	(used to show heat and angles)	50% is,
%	per cent	for example,
	(means out of every 100 parts)	$\frac{1}{2}$ of any quantity

Roman Numerals

I	 1	XI	. . . 11	XXX	. . . 30
II	 2	XII	. . . 12	XL	. . . 40
III	 3	XIII	. . . 13	L	 50
IV	 4	XIV	. . . 14	LX	. . . 60
V	 5	XV	. . . 15	LXX	. . . 70
VI	 6	XVI	. . . 16	LXXX	. . . 80
VII	. . . 7	XVII	. . . 17	XC	. . . 90
VIII	. . . 8	XVIII	. . . 18	C	 100
IX	 9	XIX	. . . 19	D	 500
X	 10	XX	. . . 20	M	. . . 1000

These symbols are combined to represent higher numbers.
For example:

XXXVI	. . 36	DCCC	. . . 800	MCM	. . 1900
DC	. . . 600	MDCCLXXIV	1774	MCMLXXX	1980

The coins we use

Bronze coins

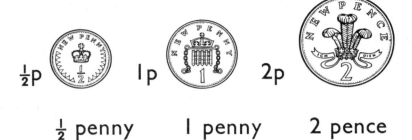

½p   1p   2p

½ penny   1 penny   2 pence

Silver coloured coins

5p

5 pence

10p

10 pence

50p

50 pence

The Monarch's head appears on all coins.

Writing money amounts

The sign for **half-penny** is $\frac{1}{2}$p
The sign for a **penny** or **pence** is p
The sign for a **pound** or **pounds** is £

1. Amounts in pence are written like this:

   72p   6p   20p

2. Amounts in pounds are written like this:

   £1   £132   £792

   Do **not** add a decimal point.

3. Amounts in pounds and pence are written with a decimal point between the pounds and the pence.
   Remember that the **p** sign is not used in amounts of £1 or more.

   £1.72   £1.05   £101.18$\frac{1}{2}$

4. When doing addition and subtraction sums in money, the decimal points should always line up like this:

   $$\begin{array}{r} £2.04\frac{1}{2} \\ + \;£1.50 \\ \hline £3.54\frac{1}{2} \end{array} \qquad \begin{array}{r} £10.58 \\ - \;£\;2.62 \\ \hline £\;7.96 \end{array}$$

Measurement

In measurement, words are used to show the multiples or fractions of the basic unit. The symbols for these units are shown in the table below.

Metric prefixes	Name	Number	Symbol
mega	million	1 000 000	**M**
kilo	thousand	1000	**k**
hecto	hundred	100	**h**
deca	ten	10	**da**
deci	tenth	$\frac{1}{10}$	**d**
centi	hundredth	$\frac{1}{100}$	**c**
milli	thousandth	$\frac{1}{1000}$	**m**

For example:

1000 grams equal 1 kilogram
  This may be written 1000g = 1kg

100 centimetres equal 1 metre
  This may be written 100cm = 1m

10 kilometres may be written as 10km

Length

The **metre** is the basic unit of length.   **m**

1 metre = 1000 **millimetres**   **mm**
This may be written 1 m = 1000 mm

1 metre = 100 **centimetres**   **cm**
This may be written 1 m = 100 cm

1 metre = 10 **decimetres**   **dm**
This may be written 1 m = 10 dm

1000 metres = 1 **kilometre**   **km**

Lengths should be written like this: 2.4 m
This is the same as 240 cm or 2 400 mm

Area

The **square metre** is the basic unit of area.

m^2 is the symbol for the **square metre**.
$3m^2$ means three square metres.

For measuring large areas of land, the
basic unit is the **hectare**.   **ha**

1 hectare = 10 000 square metres

This may be written as 1 ha = 10 000 m^2

Volume and Capacity

The **cubic centimetre** is the basic unit of volume and capacity.
cm³ is the symbol for **cubic centimetre.**

The **litre** is another basic unit of volume and capacity. It is used for measuring amounts of liquid and gas.
ℓ is the symbol for **litre.**

For small quantities of liquid
the **millilitre** is used.

1 litre = 1000 millilitres	1ℓ = 1000 ml
1 litre = 1000 cm³	1ℓ = 1000 cm³

Mass

Mass is the quantity of matter in an object.
The **kilogram** is the basic unit of mass.   **kg**
For small masses the **gram** is used.   **g**
For large masses the **tonne** is used.   **t**

1 kilogram = 1000 grams	1 kg = 1000 g
1000 kilograms = 1 tonne	1000 kg = 1 t

Celsius Temperature

C = Celsius

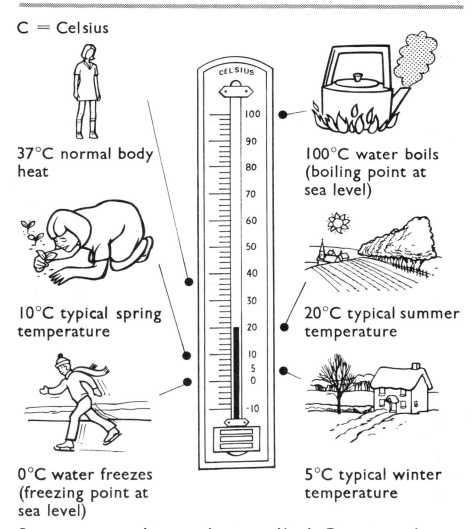

37°C normal body heat

100°C water boils (boiling point at sea level)

10°C typical spring temperature

20°C typical summer temperature

0°C water freezes (freezing point at sea level)

5°C typical winter temperature

Sometimes this scale is called Centigrade. A thermometer is used to measure temperature.

The 12-hour clock

large figures = hours   small figures = minutes

half past twelve

one o'clock

nine o'clock

quarter to three

ten past two

twenty seven minutes
to four

quarter to eleven

The meaning of a.m. and p.m.

a.m.   is the short way of writing or saying **ante meridiem.** This means the hours and minutes between midnight and midday.

p.m.   means **post meridiem.** This means the hours and minutes between midday and midnight.

Examples

1 p.m.   one o'clock in the afternoon

7.45 p.m.   45 minutes after 7 o'clock in the evening (or quarter to eight)

3.20 a.m.   twenty minutes after 3 o'clock in the morning

8.15 a.m.   15 minutes after 8 o'clock in the morning

12.30 a.m.   half an hour after midnight

12.05 p.m.   5 minutes after midday

The 24-hour clock

As we all know, although our clocks are divided into 12 hours, a whole day contains 24 hours. In some countries, a 24-hour system of telling the time is commonly used.

This clock shows how a 12-hour clock-face is used to count the hours up to 24. The small numbers inside the big ones are used to tell the time after midday until midnight.

Examples

13.05   5 minutes after 1 o'clock in the afternoon

16.00   4 o'clock in the afternoon

23.30   half past 11 o'clock at night

The 24-hour clock

before noon
a.m.

noon

after noon
p.m.

midnight

one o'clock
1 a.m.   01.00
1 p.m.   13.00

half past three
3.30 a.m.   03.30
3.30 p.m.   15.30

five minutes to twelve
11.55 a.m.   11.55
11.55 p.m.   23.55

five minutes past twelve
12.05 a.m.   00.05
12.05 p.m.   12.05

twenty minutes past three
3.20 a.m.   03.20
3.20 p.m.   15.20

twenty minutes to nine
8.40 a.m.   08.40
8.40 p.m.   20.40

The Digital Clock Face

Unlike most clock faces which are divided into 12 parts, each representing one hour, digital clocks show the hours and the minutes by numbers only. The numbers are divided into hours and minutes by one or two dots.

hours   10 : 37   minutes

The number or numbers before the dots show the time in hours. The second pair show the time in minutes. Most digital clocks show up to 12 hours only. Some also show seconds. These are in small numbers .

12 : 00
twelve o'clock
(midday *or* midnight)

1 : 30
half past one
or one thirty

10 : 45
quarter to eleven *or*
ten forty-five

11 : 59
one minute to twelve *or*
eleven fifty-nine

Divisions of time

60 seconds . . . . . . 1 minute
60 minutes . . . . . . 1 hour
24 hours . . . . 1 day

A day means 1 day and 1 night

7 days = a week   13 weeks = a quarter
2 weeks = a fortnight 52 weeks = a year
4 weeks = a month*   12 months = a year

*Months vary in length. They may have 28, 29, 30 or 31 days.

Learn the rhyme on page 30

Months

1. January   5. May   9. September
2. February   6. June   10. October
3. March   7. July   11. November
4. April   8. August   12. December

Number of days in the months

Thirty days hath September,
April, June and November,
All the rest have thirty-one,
Excepting February alone,
Which has twenty-eight days clear,
And twenty-nine in each leap-year.

Number of days in the year

Ordinary years have 365 days.

Leap-years have 366 days.

Leap-year comes every fourth year, when 1 day (the 29th of February) is added to make 366 days.

If the number of a year can be divided exactly by 4, it is a leap-year.

Examples: 1980   1984   1988

The names of the seasons

spring   summer   autumn   winter

In the United States and Canada autumn is called 'the Fall'.

The year as a calendar

	January							**February**							**March**				
S	.	3	10	17	24	31	.	7	14	21	28	.	.	7	14	21	28	.
M	.	4	11	18	25	.	1	8	15	22	.	.	1	8	15	22	29	.
Tu	.	5	12	19	26	.	2	9	16	23	.	.	2	9	16	23	30	.
W	.	6	13	20	27	.	3	10	17	24	.	.	3	10	17	24	31	.
Th	.	7	14	21	28	.	4	11	18	25	.	.	4	11	18	25	.	.
F	1	8	15	22	29	.	5	12	19	26	.	.	5	12	19	26	.	.
S	2	9	16	23	30	.	6	13	20	27	.	.	6	13	20	27	.	.

	April							**May**							**June**				
S	.	4	11	18	25	.	.	2	9	16	23	30	.	6	13	20	27	.
M	.	5	12	19	26	.	.	3	10	17	24	31	.	7	14	21	28	.
Tu	.	6	13	20	27	.	.	4	11	18	25	.	1	8	15	22	29	.
W	.	7	14	21	28	.	.	5	12	19	26	.	2	9	16	23	30	.
Th	1	8	15	22	29	.	.	6	13	20	27	.	3	10	17	24	.	.
F	2	9	16	23	30	.	.	7	14	21	28	.	4	11	18	25	.	.
S	3	10	17	24	.	.	1	8	15	22	29	.	5	12	19	26	.	.

	July							**August**							**September**				
S	.	4	11	18	25	.	1	8	15	22	29	.	.	5	12	19	26	.
M	.	5	12	19	26	.	2	9	16	23	30	.	.	6	13	20	27	.
Tu	.	6	13	20	27	.	3	10	17	24	31	.	.	7	14	21	28	.
W	.	7	14	21	28	.	4	11	18	25	.	.	1	8	15	22	29	.
Th	1	8	15	22	29	.	5	12	19	26	.	.	2	9	16	23	30	.
F	2	9	16	23	30	.	6	13	20	27	.	.	3	10	17	24	.	.
S	3	10	17	24	31	.	7	14	21	28	.	.	4	11	18	25	.	.

	October							**November**							**December**				
S	.	3	10	17	24	31	.	7	14	21	28	.	.	5	12	19	26	.
M	.	4	11	18	25	.	1	8	15	22	29	.	.	6	13	20	27	.
Tu	.	5	12	19	26	.	2	9	16	23	30	.	.	7	14	21	28	.
W	.	6	13	20	27	.	3	10	17	24	.	.	1	8	15	22	29	.
Th	.	7	14	21	28	.	4	11	18	25	.	.	2	9	16	23	30	.
F	1	8	15	22	29	.	5	12	19	26	.	.	3	10	17	24	31	.
S	2	9	16	23	30	.	6	13	20	27	.	.	4	11	18	25	.	.

The first day of the year can be any day of the week. So can all the other dates. When the year is divided into 52 weeks one day is left over. This makes the next year start a day later, or, in the case of a leap-year, two days later.

Fractions

⬤ ▬	whole	1
◑ ▭	half	$\dfrac{1}{2}$
◕ ▭	quarter	$\dfrac{1}{4}$
◔ ▭	three-quarters	$\dfrac{3}{4}$
✳ ▭	eighth	$\dfrac{1}{8}$
◔ ▭	third	$\dfrac{1}{3}$
◕ ▭	two-thirds	$\dfrac{2}{3}$
✦ ▭	one-fifth	$\dfrac{1}{5}$
✳ ▭	one-tenth	$\dfrac{1}{10}$

Fractions, decimals and percentages

fraction		decimal	percentage
1	whole	1.00	100%
$\frac{1}{2}$	half	0.50	50%
$\frac{1}{4}$	quarter	0.25	25%
$\frac{3}{4}$	three-quarters	0.75	75%
$\frac{1}{3}$	third	0.3333...	$33\frac{1}{3}$%
$\frac{2}{3}$	two-thirds	0.6666...	$66\frac{2}{3}$%
$\frac{1}{5}$	fifth	0.20	20%
$\frac{1}{8}$	eighth	0.125	$12\frac{1}{2}$%
$\frac{1}{10}$	tenth	0.10	10%
$\frac{1}{20}$	twentieth	0.05	5%
$\frac{1}{25}$	twenty-fifth	0.04	4%
$\frac{1}{50}$	fiftieth	0.02	2%
$\frac{1}{100}$	hundredth	0.01	1%

recurring

Measuring: useful words

measuring	thin	small
wide	long	huge
width	length	big
broad	short	tall
breadth	deep	high
narrow	depth	height
thick	shallow	low

Quantity: useful words

amount	lot	most
huge	little	less
great	few	least
large	several	double
much	some	pair
many	more	same

Volume and Mass: useful words

weight	full	light
weigh	empty	heavy

Time: useful words

hour	year	ancient
minute	yesterday	new
second	today	modern
day	tomorrow	fast
morning	past	quick
afternoon	present	quickly
evening	future	slow
night	age	slowly
week	century	early
month	old	late

Position: useful words

first	top	up
last	bottom	down
next	above	forward
begin	over	back
start	under	front
finish	underneath	before
left	beneath	behind
right	below	beside
middle	inside	far
side	outside	near

Space and Area: useful words

round	half	shape
circle	quarter	size
square	part	across
edge	piece	corner

Measuring angles

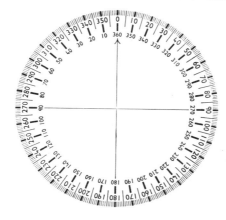

A circular protractor.

Many protractors are semi-circular or half circles.

Protractors are used to measure angles. The edge of a protractor is divided into 360 equal parts. Each part is called a **degree**. The number of degrees is written with a small ° following the figure, like this:

45°   75°

An **angle** is the measurement of the turn between two lines which meet like this:

60°   135°

This is a right angle. It is 90°
Four times 90° make 360°

90°

Names of plane shapes

rhombus a four-sided plane figure with all sides of the same length. Opposite angles are equal but none are right angles.

square

rhombus

rhombus

rectangle a four-sided plane figure. All interior angles are right angles.

parallelogram a four-sided figure having both pairs of opposite sides parallel and equal in length.

rectangle

parallelogram

parallelogram

ellipse a plane figure like a flattened circle.

circle

ellipse (oval)

ellipse (oval)

trapezium a four-sided plane figure with only one pair of opposite sides parallel.

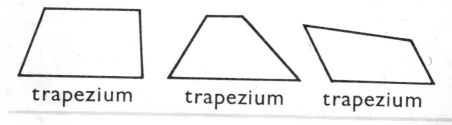

trapezium

trapezium

trapezium

triangle a plane figure with three sides, having three interior angles which added together equal two right angles.

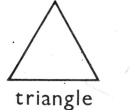 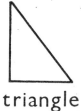 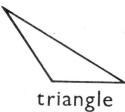

triangle   triangle   triangle

pentagon a plane figure bounded by five sides which may or may not be of the same length.

 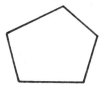 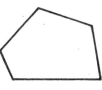

pentagon   pentagon   pentagon

hexagon a plane figure bounded by six sides which may or may not be of the same length.

 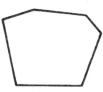

hexagon   hexagon   hexagon

octagon a plane figure bounded by eight sides which may or may not be of the same length.

octagon   octagon   octagon

Names of solid shapes

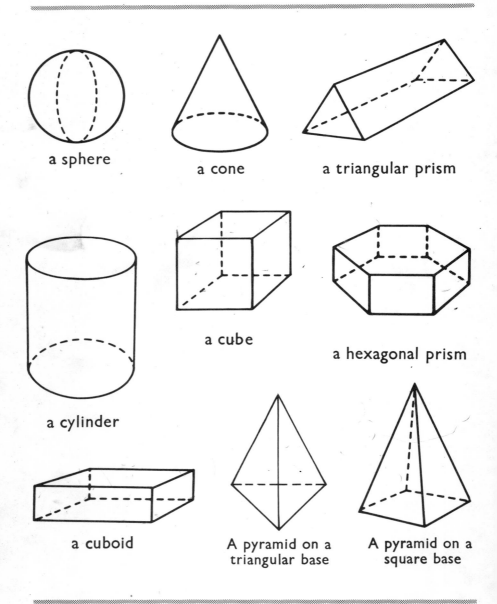

a sphere

a cone

a triangular prism

a cylinder

a cube

a hexagonal prism

a cuboid

A pyramid on a
triangular base

A pyramid on a
square base